Stop Hypochondri?

CW00539318

Hypochondriacs – unders
and free yourself from it

Including a self-test and instructions for self-help

©2020, Lutz Schneider

Expertengruppe Verlag

Stop Hypochondria

Hypochondriacs – understand your fear of diseases and free yourself from it

Including a self-test and instructions for self-help

Publisher: Expertengruppe Verlag

CONTENTS

About the author 9

Preface 11

What is hypochondria? 19

Secondary hypochondria 22

When are you considered to be a hypochondriac?
.... 23

Are you a hypochondriac? 25

Self-test 26

Analysis: 29

How common is hypochondria? 31

Who is affected? 33

Which subtypes are there? 35

Olfactory reference syndrome 36

Delusional parasitosis 37

Dysmorphophobia..................................... 38

Bowel movement hypochondria.............. 39

Fear of sickness 40

Environmental hypochondria 42

Cyberchondria 43

How does hypochondria manifest itself? 45

Observing the symptoms 47

Doctor visits... 49

Health screening 51

Illusory sicknesses and affected organs 52

What are the causes of hypochondria? 54

Trigger in childhood 55

Experience with sickness and death 56

Unresolved inner conflicts 57

Upbringing based on fear.......................... 58

Influencing factors 59

Excessive belief in an existing sickness 60

Low self-esteem 61

Desire for attention................................. 62

Emotional instability 63

Emotional blindness................................. 65

Stress 67

Dysfunctional personal defence mechanism   69

Media 70

Personal experience of a sickness............ 71

Genetic Factors 72

How do you recognise hypochondria? 73

Examinations by the psychiatrist or psychologist. 75

Criteria for the diagnosis.. 76

Two divisions... 78

Distinction from other sicknesses.......................... 79

Mild hypochondriacal worries 80

Somatoform disorders 81

Delusional disorders................................. 82

Panic disorder 83

General fear disorder 84

Illness phobia 85

Compulsive disorder 86

Organic sickness....................................... 87

Fear of progression 88

Common comorbidities (accompanying illnesses) 89

Depression 90

Anxiety disorders 91

Somatoform disorders 92

Effects of hypochondria 93

Personal effects.. 94

Physical effects.. 95

Social impact 96

Treatment of hypochondria.....................................97

Cognitive behavioural psychotherapy 99

Psychotherapy....................................... 101

Psycho-sensory procedures 102

Medicinal therapy 103

Progression and prognosis in hypochondria....... 104

Liberate yourself from your fears in four stages 105

Step 1: Observation... 107

Diary 108

Step 2: Insight... 109

Medical consultation.............................. 110

Diagnostic findings in black and white... 111

Talk to relatives 112

Step 3: Mind control 113

Positive affirmation................................ 114

Step 4: Stabilisation... 118

Sport and physical activity 119

Yoga and meditation 121

Relaxation techniques............................. 123

Relaxation techniques with instructions...................124

Progressive Muscle Relaxation 125

Aim 127

Applications.. 128

Contraindications 129

The 2 areas of PMR 130

Instructions 132

Autogenic training.. 137

Contraindications 141

The 3 basic steps of autogenic training . 142

The 7 Basic formulae.............................. 144

Instructions 146

Tips for relatives..150

Summary 154

Did you enjoy my book?..159

Book Recommendations 161

References...167

Disclaimer...171

ABOUT THE AUTHOR

Lutz Schneider lives with his wife, Evelyn, in an old farmhouse in beautiful Rhineland.

Ever since he studied the biology of evolution, over 20 years ago, he has been interested in marginal health subjects, which are often hidden from the main stream, but which are scientifically well accepted. He teaches this knowledge, not only to his students, but also reaches a wider audience in Germany with his various publications.

In his books, he speaks about subjects, the positive effects of which are widely unknown and on which he can pass on his own experiences. All of his publications, therefore, are based on indisputable scientific facts, but also encompass his own very personal experiences and knowledge. This way, the reader not only receives factual information about the subject but also a practical guide with a wide range of knowledge and useful tips, which are easy to understand and put into practice.

Lutz Schneider's easy to read work puts the reader into a relaxed and pleasant ambience, while gaining insight into a subject which few know anything about but which everyone could profit from.

PREFACE

Your hands are shaking – is it a sign of a neurological disease? Your stomach aches – is it a sign of colon cancer? And the cold from a few days ago – could it be the first sign of a serious immune disorder?

Have you asked yourself such questions when you have felt unwell? I used to preoccupy myself with these types of questions every day. I would like to tell you my story and show you how I helped free myself from my fears.

Perhaps some of my stories are recognisable to you, or perhaps you have been experiencing something else. Every experience is different. This short summary of my personal story may help you to understand how I came to write this book.

I cannot remember exactly how it began. I think there were already short phases of hypochondria during my childhood, but I do not remember them all that clearly. However, I do remember a few episodes from that time.

One episode, that I can remember, was as follows: As a child, I was watching a film about two brothers. One of the brothers had a tumour and had lost his hair during chemotherapy. I could not get to sleep easily for weeks after that, because I thought that I could feel something in my head, that I would get sick and lose all of my hair. It got so bad, that I could hardly concentrate at school. I began getting lots of headaches and became afraid, that I would get sick and about the following therapy where I would lose all my hair. It was only after confiding in my mother, that I was able to discard the fear and begin to live a normal life, doing things which were interesting at my age.

Sometime later, there was a further episode which I can remember: I had read a book, a true story about a girl of my age, who was presenting with the initial symptoms of multiple sclerosis. For example, when she was passing the butter across the table during a meal, it fell out of her hands for no apparent reason. Her hand felt limp and different. At first, her parents did not believe her, but as her symptoms progressed, she was diagnosed by a doctor with multiple sclerosis.

After I had read this book, I was sure I had got multiple sclerosis. The girl was the same age as me and sometimes things slipped out of my hands too. On close inspection, I noticed a feeling of numbness and limpness in my hand. Then I got a tingling sensation and I started to panic. I told my mother, who was able to calm me down and the fear began to fade.

While I was a teenager, I did not overly suffer from strong fears or such things, apart from the normal puberty problems. This period in my life passed relatively peacefully. I was very well connected socially, had a lot of friends, I was active and was involved in a lot of activities.

After my vocational training, my friends scattered somewhat and I moved away from town as I started my new job. For the first time in my life, I felt a little lonely, because my friends and family were further away and contact with them became more sporadic. My job needed a lot of my attention and did not leave me much free time and so I took part in a lot less activities.

Then, while I was a young adult, there were a few problems in my career, which were bothering me and at the same time, my uncle became very ill with cancer. He was suffering from pancreatic cancer, which was not treatable, once the doctors had found it.

The first fears for my own health crept up on me slowly. Through the stress I was feeling about my job, I often suffered from tension headaches. Now I can tell you, that these were tension headaches, but during that time, I started to worry that I had a tumour.

I assume today, that the fact that my uncle's tumour had been discovered so late caused me increased anxiety. I kept asking myself: What, if the tumour is already so far advanced, that I will not be able to have any remedial therapy?

The internet was the best source to Google my headache and I kept receiving the confirmation, that it could be a tumour, as well as a great number of other things. If I became dizzy or had coordination difficulties, this caused me great anxiety that the tumour had increased in size and that was why the symptoms were increasing.

The daily search and preoccupation with my symptoms probably served to distract me from the problems with

my work. I presume, that I was unintentionally trans-
ferring my problems from one place to another. While
I was engrossed in my physical condition, I did not need
to worry about my worries at work.

During this time, I often visited the doctor. I first went
to the family practitioner, then to a neurologist in
order to find the reason for my headaches. Various
scans were made of my skull, which never gave any
hint of a tumour. Despite that, I believed, that the
doctors must have overlooked something.

My family and friends started to become less
concerned about my negative results and I did not feel
that the doctors were taking me seriously enough, nor
did my closest associates. My reaction to that was to
withdraw into myself.

My mother was always the one, who was able to lead
me away from my fears when I was a child, and this
time it was the same. Even though I kept ignoring her,
she continued to try and find a way to influence me.
She told me she was very troubled, that I was allowing
my fears to rule my life. On many occasions she
encouraged me to deal with my fears and not to

concentrate on the symptoms I was supposedly experiencing.

At one point, I was sitting alone at home, looking at my laptop and I asked myself what had happened to me. I realised, that I had totally changed I hardly went out and was not interacting with my friends. It suddenly went "klick" and I said to myself, that I did not want to go on like that.

A few days later, I started to think about how I envisaged the rest of my life. I thought I would like to return to my old activities, free of fear. After about 4 days, I made another appointment by the doctor, this one was going to be the last for some time.

The talk with the doctor confirmed what my mother had been trying to tell me. The fear was making me sick, not the symptoms themselves. I asked to get all the pictures and reports of my examinations and I read them in black and white. Slowly, I was able to free myself from the notion, that I was sick and was able to believe the results of the reports.

My doctor suggested various therapy possibilities. I had made up my mind, that I was going to do it alone.

My promise to my doctors was that, if I failed, I would come back. My mother was at my side and helped me along the way. However, I did agree to make an appointment a few weeks later, to check my condition and see if I really was able to reduce my anxieties. This was my insurance policy, so that I did not fall back into believing my old fears and believing that I was sick.

After my appointment, I met with my mother to tell her about what was said and what I intended to do about it. She seemed relieved and promised to support me. And so I began to take my healing into my own hands and it worked.

The next time I saw the doctor, he said I was unrecognisable. The change that I had made was admirable. He asked me how I had done it, my strategy seemed to impress him.

My success in finding my own way to recognise my condition and to work on my fears, gave me back my self-esteem and quality of life.

I hope, that you will experience the same. I would like to show you how I did it in my book and to help you, too, to find a way back into normal life, free from fears.

My mother was, and still is, wonderfully supportive and I would like to thank her for that. I hope you two have wonderful relatives, who can help you to find your way, just like I do. I realise, that I am more the exception than the rule with this, because most suffers are not able to find their way out of their problems without professional help.

I wish you much success.

For the sake of simplicity, I have used the masculine form in my writing although, of course, I mean to include females, too.

This is a guidebook, based on my own experience, together with materials from research I have done and lectures I have given. Despite that, it remains a personal guidebook and is not standard medical literature. My method does not replace a visit to the doctor or therapist and their treatments.

- Chapter 1 -

WHAT IS HYPOCHONDRIA?

Hypochondria is one of the most interesting diseases known to man and dates well back into the days of ancient medicine.

The word "Hypochondria" is Greek and means something like "under the cartilage". The cartilage around the ribs is meant here, because it was believed, that the region around the diaphragm was known, not only as the centre of the spirit but also the home of melancholy.

This belief continued until the 19th Century. Later, there were new interpretations, which suggested, that hypochondria was "the mildest form of madness", a type of "melancholy", or a "partial occurrence of neurasthenic syndrome".

Today we know hypochondria as the fear of disease or of being ill. If you suffer from this, you believe, that you are suffering from a most significant form of an illness by listening to the smallest changes in your bodily functions.

Constantly, or in phases, your thoughts are preoccupied and you believe that you are suffering from a serious illness. A common cold could be a sign of a serious immune sickness, such as AIDS; headaches are signs of a brain tumour; constipation is the first sign of colon cancer. These are only a few examples of many.

The sufferer either goes to the doctor very often to have his symptoms checked or he avoids going to the doctor altogether, because he is afraid of having his fears confirmed.

The pathological fear of sickness, which can significantly reduce the quality of your life, can be very similar to a panic attack. However, hypochondria is considered to be a psychosomatic disease. This means, that it is a psychological illness, which causes physical symptoms. The patient, for example, may have the suspicion, that he is suffering from a tumour on his bladder. Whilst concentrating on his own bladder activity, the behaviour of the bladder changes, caused by the patient suffering from stress and not through a physical sickness. Despite that, the sufferer feels, that his suspicions have been confirmed.

There is disagreement as to whether hypochondria is a psychosomatic disease, because the physical symptoms are not the main cause of the sickness but often accompany it.

SECONDARY HYPOCHONDRIA

If there is a primary sickness present, such as an anxiety disorder or schizophrenia, and hypochondria results from that sickness, this is known in medical terms as a secondary hypochondria. However, the symptoms themselves do not constitute an illness.

WHEN ARE YOU CONSIDERED TO BE A HYPOCHONDRIAC?

The term 'hypochondria' is very broad. It begins with an acute consciousness of one's own health and the taking of precautionary behaviour, but can lead to hypochondriacal mania.

Those, who listen to their bodies, take their health seriously. However, the borderline to becoming a hypochondriac is not far away. A hypochondriac is not a person, who takes vitamin pills every day or is afraid, that he has got a bit of a cold after visiting the swimming pool the day before. As a hypochondriac, you have much greater fears, for example, that you have cancer or another serious illness.

If the first thought after you wake up is: "How do I feel?". If you ask yourself "Are the headaches or stomach pains strong today?" or "Is my hand shaking more today?", this suggests, that your thoughts are hypochondriacal. Your thoughts and everyday life are filled with permanent fear. That is probably the biggest difference between a hypochondriac and a health-conscious person. The latter is able to live his life in a healthy way without suffering permanently from negative thoughts.

But where exactly is the borderline and when does it become pathological? That is generally very difficult to say.

ARE YOU A HYPOCHONDRIAC?

Have you often asked yourself, if your behaviour is normal or whether you are already a hypochondriac? Or do the people around you think you tend towards being a hypochondriac?

The borderline is sometimes not clear to see. Everyone worries from time to time about his health. One sign, that you are not following the norm is, if you notice that your thoughts are making you ill, or that you are not able to do things, that you could previously do. Perhaps also, your social interactions have changed.

SELF-TEST

The following self-test could give you an idea whether your fears or behaviour towards sicknesses are within normal boundaries or lean more towards having a hypochondriacal condition.

This test can only give you a hint of your current status and cannot replace a diagnosis by a psychologist or doctor. Not every one of the indicators listed needs to be caused by hypochondria. You should always let an expert decide on that. If you have the suspicion, that you are suffering from hypochondria, I suggest strongly, that you find an expert in the field.

This test is not suitable for sick or chronically sick people with a doctor's diagnosis to prove it, or for people, who have recovered, or are recovering, from a serious illness.

Answer the following questions with "yes" or "no". Take a note of the number of times you have answered "yes". Answer spontaneously, without thinking too much about the question.

1. Do you often worry, that you may have a serious illness?

2. Do you suffer from many different pains or signs of sickness?

3. Do you often notice variations in your bodily functions? (digestion, heart)

4. If you hear from acquaintances, or through the media, about a sickness, are you then afraid, that you may also have that sickness?

5. Do you feel, that people around you are not taking you seriously enough when you are feeling ill?

6. Do you mistrust your doctor when he tells you everything is alright?

7. Do you think, that you worry more about your health than other people do?

8. Are you afraid, that there is something seriously wrong with your body, but despite that, the doctors do not appear to recognise it?

9. Do you often control your blood pressure and pulse or carry out self-tests?

10. Do you often change your doctor because you do not trust him?

ANALYSIS:

You have answered all the questions. Count how many times you have answered with "yes". The number of "yes" answers will give you an idea of your current condition.

1 to 2: All clear! You probably do not suffer from hypochondria. Your feelings towards your body are within the normal range. You worry from time to time about your health. Sometimes you may think, that you have a sickness, but it fades again. Perhaps you have changed your doctor, because you did not trust him, but that has not happened very frequently. Feeling a responsible consciousness towards your health is very important. Keep it up!

3 to 4: Caution! You listen to your body very intensively and seem to be very sensitive to its processes. It seems to hinder you from time to time in your every-day activities, but does not dictate everything you do. I recommend speaking to a doctor or psychologist in order to avoid an increase in the symptoms.

5 to 10: Warning! The fear of sickness is hindering your thoughts and actions very intensively. Your life and your well-being are probably being significantly

impaired by your fear of sickness. If you have not already contacted a qualified specialist about your feelings and symptoms, I recommend, that you contact a doctor or psychologist as quickly as possible.

HOW COMMON IS HYPOCHONDRIA?

Throughout history there have been examples of people with hypochondria. These include Charlie Chaplin, Frederick the Great, Woody Allen and Thomas Mann.

Below are a few statistics, which show, that hypochondria is more common than you may think:

- In Germany, approximately 1% of the population suffers from hypochondria. That is about 820,000 people!

- The most severe form, the hypochondriacal mania, is suffered by about 0.5%. That calculates at 5 out of every 10,000 people, who are affected. (In Germany, that amounts to about 4,100 people).

- About 6% of Germans suffer from some form of light health-related fears.

- A quarter of all patients who attend university psychotherapeutic outpatients are hypochondriacs.

- Somewhere between 2% and 7% of all patients attending German general practitioners are hypochondriacs.

- A similar number of men and women suffer from hypochondria.

The total number of sufferers is difficult to estimate because there is relatively little research in this field and because many sufferers do not seek professional help, due to embarrassment.

There could be a large number of unrecorded cases. Many sufferers do not go to the doctor because for fear of receiving confirmation of their sickness, so they are not recorded in the health system and are not part of the statistics. However, in most cases, the sufferer tends to visit the doctor unusually often. This also puts a great financial strain on the health system.

WHO IS AFFECTED?

Up to now, no exact figures are available about the age of the sufferer when the sickness first appears. About a third of those questioned stated, that they were already fighting fears of certain sicknesses during childhood.

It can, however, be said, that a similar number of men and women suffer from the condition.

There are people, who develop hypochondriacal attacks after a serious illness. It occurs particularly in people, who have just recovered from a serious illness and who develop fears of having a relapse or of contracting a new sickness. That could develop into hypochondria because they know their physical processes very well and are sensitive to any changes.

People, who have witnessed the serious illness of a person close to them, can also become hypo-chondriacs. Fears for their own health develop and suddenly, more and more symptoms are perceived, which could be similar to those of the sick person or could be symptoms of a completely different sickness.

People who have lost their trust in the health system or doctors, because of wrong diagnoses or late diagnosis of a sickness, can also become affected.

Some sufferers may have already suffered from a traumatic experience. This can also play a role in the development of hypochondria.

It is also possible to fall into phases of hypochondria through an increase in access to new information about health and sicknesses. This mostly affects medical students or people, who are training in the health services, such as nursing staff. It is not atypical for students, who are learning about a particular sickness, to suffer from exactly the symptoms, which they are reading about. In most cases, this is a temporary phenomenon and will quickly disappear.

Statistics show, that many people, who watch health programmes on TV, feel unwell after the programme has finished and worry more about suffering from a sickness.

However, it is something, which can affect anyone, whether they have had medical training, a previous sickness or anything similar.

WHICH SUBTYPES ARE THERE?

There are various sub-groups of hypochondria. They distinguish themselves by their symptoms. However, their treatment remains similar to that of the "classical" hypochondriac.

In the following pages, the main sub-groups of hypochondria are introduced briefly.

OLFACTORY REFERENCE SYNDROME

The olfactory reference syndrome, also known as Bromosis, is the persistent false belief of emitting abnormal body odour, which the sufferer believes is foul and offensive to other individuals.

The origin of this syndrome can be connected to other overriding diseases, such as schizophrenia, compulsive disorders or an organic injury to the brain.

The patient often has the feeling, that the gestures, facial expressions and behaviour of other people result from his offensive body odour.

Often, there follows an obsessive search for an organic sickness, which would explain this subjectively-experienced body odour.

People excessively use perfumes and deodorants to cover up the smell. The fear of offending others negatively impacts the social behaviour of the sufferer, they experience embarrassment and withdraw from society. They do not feel able to socialise with others.

DELUSIONAL PARASITOSIS

Simply put, it is the skin-insect-syndrome, also known amongst experts as Parasitosis. It happens where a person incorrectly believes, that living organisms, mostly worms, spiders or insects are to be found under the skin and are moving around. This leads to fear and itchiness.

Among the verifiable causes of this syndrome are cocaine abuse, amphetamine abuse, alcohol with-drawal with delirium and conditions of the central nervous system and brain damage.

DYSMORPHOPHOBIA

People, who suffer from this syndrome, believe, that they are either possessed, malformed or disfigured, or just plain repulsively ugly. They are preoccupied with the thought, that the slightest deviation from the norm, such as hair loss or a mole, could have serious consequences. This has a negative impact on their social and work life.

BOWEL MOVEMENT HYPOCHONDRIA

In this type of hypochondria, particular attention is paid by the sufferer to his bowel movements. He concentrates solely on his digestion and knows exactly when and how often he has been to the toilet. He will also pay attention to the composition of the bowel movement and any accompanying symptoms, such as gas discharge.

FEAR OF SICKNESS

Fear of sickness is known by experts as nosophobia and is a hypochondriacal disorder, which is long-term and does not necessarily result in an acute anxiety state. Despite its name, it is not a phobia-type disorder in the true sense of the word, but an anxiety disorder.

People suffering from nosophobia have a strong fear or belief, that they are suffering from an illness, even though there are no, or very few, objective medical indications.

The sufferer is very conscious of all body functions and is very sensitive towards anything, which deviates from the norm. Unfortunately, this could be mis- or over-interpreted, leading to the sufferer imagining, that he has an illness, although there are little or no indications of this.

However, the sufferer is not delusional. He knows, that there are few indications for his fears. This is the difference between someone suffering from noso-phobia and someone with hypochondria. As a hypochondriac, you cannot tell the difference between fear of a sickness and the sickness itself. Hypo-chondriacs strongly believe, that they have the sickness and can feel the symptoms. However, even if they know, that they are only suffering from the fear of sickness, it can still be agonising. You know, that the fear is irrational, but you cannot tear yourself away from the thoughts circling around you about the sickness.

Nosophobia is also not to be confused with myso-phobia, even if both disorders often appear together. If you are suffering from mysophobia, you are afraid of being infected by germs or bacteria from bad food, dirt or rubbish, not so much believing, that you are suffering from an illness. You would suffer short panic attacks in the face of specific events.

ENVIRONMENTAL HYPOCHONDRIA

If you suffer from environmental hypochondria, the main source of your fears is the environment. In the past, such fears could have been of thunder or lightning, which seemed threatening. Today people fear more of being negatively influenced by electro-magnetic waves, such as electro smog or radioactive rays, or chronic poisoning caused by, for example, amalgam. Other diverse chemical substances, which may be considered allergenic, can also cause fears and anxiety.

What all environmental influences, which lead to fears, have in common is, that they are invisible and cannot be proven. Contrary to visible causes, which have a harmful influence on people, such as nicotine, alcohol, sunlight or gases, invisible, uncontrollable influences are considered to be more of a threat.

There are interest groups, which make the environ-mental hypochondria even worse, for example by their aggressive presence in the media, in an attempt to obtain recognition of their beliefs.

CYBERCHONDRIA

The term "cyberchondria" is derived from the words "cyber" and "hypochondria" and describes a physical state of anxiety in people, whose conditions are caused by over-zealous research for symptoms in the internet. The already present hypochondriacal tendencies of the sufferer are strengthened by the onset of cyberchondria. You could call this a modern form of hypochondria.

You will probably recognise this: You quickly pull out your mobile phone, enter your symptoms and within seconds you have been given a plethora of possible sicknesses, which fit to the symptoms you have entered. Intensive research for information in medical books is probably now a thing of the past. Today, almost all information is researched on the internet, because it is quick and simple.

Research in the internet can be a problem though, it offers a confusing variety of information about sicknesses. In addition, not all sources are reliable.

As a hypochondriac, the fear of the information available obtained from other sufferers, and the comments found on forums and chats multiplies the situation. When you read about a person, who is also sick, this gives a more realistic touch than just reading in text books about it. You identify yourself with that person and the sickness and the belief of the existence of the sickness increases dramatically.

For those of us, who are not experts, the internet can be useful in categorising your symptoms and obtaining ideas for treatment. However, for people with existing fear of sickness, this can be dangerous because the wide range of information is bewildering, and any existing fears could seem to be confirmed.

So, the sickness can be triggered or strengthened through use of the internet. On top of that, there is the potential danger of addiction, that can occur through using the internet for hours each day.

- Chapter 2 -

HOW DOES HYPOCHONDRIA MANIFEST ITSELF?

The central aspect with hypochondriacs is their great fear of sickness. In addition to the fear of sickness they also suffer from fear of pain, disability, suffering and death.

You are experiencing symptoms and the insecurity, that you feel because of it, is almost unbearable. You have a great urge to find out what is causing your symptoms. Your physical symptoms seem to be increasing and you are watching out for the slightest change in your body.

As a hypochondriac, you feel symptoms, which you relate to a particular sickness and you are convinced, that you are suffering from it. The insecurity and anxiety, which this causes, can lead to serious panic attacks.

This can significantly impact the quality of your life, if you are continually in fear of having a sickness present in your body. You spend a lot of time on the internet researching, collecting information about your own symptoms. Your thoughts are almost consumed by the fear of getting the sickness and this takes up most of the time in your daily life. This, in turn, impacts your life significantly.

OBSERVING THE SYMPTOMS

Soon you find yourself in a vicious circle, which you will have difficulty getting out of. It starts with you noticing every small change in your physical processes, for example rashes, swellings, sweat build-up, pounding heart or any small pain. You find the discovery to be unpleasant and believe, that it could be the symptom of a sickness.

After that, you start to pay particular attention to the affected area of your body. This, in turn, increases the probability, that you will discover more symptoms.

Again, you misinterpret the symptoms because you immediately believe, that they must be caused by a serious illness.

The observations and examinations increase and further controls are added, such as weight control or intensive physical examination of the affected area.

This, in turn, leads to the symptoms becoming more uncomfortable and you make it even worse by constantly poking at the area.

Often, you research the observed symptoms, the confirmation that they could be due to a serious illness is strengthened and this increases the anxiety level.

DOCTOR VISITS

Hypochondriacs go to the doctor very often. They want to find out, what the symptoms they are experiencing are caused by. Because of that, they go to the doctor more and more frequently. If the doctor says, that the sufferer should not worry about his symptoms and that he is healthy, this reassures the patient short-term, but the symptoms and the anxiety return very quickly.

The patient then does not feel, that the doctor is taking him seriously enough, which causes him frustration and dissatisfaction. He often asks himself questions, such as "Why does my doctor not recognise that I am suffering?". This in turn causes him to search for another doctor, and so on, until the question becomes "Which doctor, if any, will acknowledge that I am suffering?", a question, which he will repeat all the time, while 'doctor-hopping'.

Many sufferers do self-testing, such as measuring the blood pressure or pulse and self-palpation (poking at the affected spot). Friends and family are often asked their opinion about the suspected sickness symptoms.

This can also lead to frustration, if the sufferer does not feel, that his concerns are being taken seriously.

There are also hypochondriacs, who avoid the doctor, clinics and hospitals, even cemeteries at all costs in order to avoid confrontation with their fears and having their fears confirmed by a doctor.

If the doctor prescribes a therapy for a particular sickness, it often happens, that the condition of the patient deteriorates, rather than improves. Sometimes, complications and side effects can be added through the taking of medicines, which may cause the condition to worsen. The sufferer often discovers new symptoms. The result of the therapy is unsatisfactory, both for the doctor and the sufferer.

HEALTH SCREENING

One positive aspect of being a hypochondriac is, that they tend to live very healthy lives. They often do not smoke or drink, fearing lung cancer or liver sclerosis.

A sufferer often takes care, that he has a healthy diet and some also participate in sports. However, over time, he tends to do less and less sport, fearing a deterioration in his physical condition.

The sufferer hopes, that through having a healthy lifestyle, he can at least minimise the risk of becoming sick, and this is something he can influence himself.

ILLUSORY SICKNESSES AND AFFECTED ORGANS

The most feared sicknesses are nearly always serious conditions. Most often it is cancer, which is most feared, followed by serious heart conditions and disorders, then conditions of the muscle or nervous systems.

Under the different cancer diseases, brain, skin, breast, lung and also abdominal cancers are suspected the most. With women, cancers are also feared in gynaecological organs, such as those of the ovary or womb. Heart attacks and serious heart valve conditions or aneurysms are the most likely heart conditions suspected whereas multiple sclerosis or ALS are the most likely neurological conditions to be suspected by hypochondriacs.

Particularly when fear of cancer sicknesses is present, such as breast, skin or lymph gland cancer, the sufferer often examines himself in an attempt to discover any changes. Sometimes, however, this can make the symptoms worse. For example, if he examines his lymphatic nodes by exerting pressure on the lymphatic tissue and repeats the exercise often, because he thinks they are swollen, this often results in the lymphatic nodes becoming swollen because of the constant pressure exerted by the sufferer. This, in turn, leads to the anxiety growing because the lymph glands are getting bigger, which leads to more examinations.

Hypochondriacs are very well informed about their supposed sicknesses and, as in the example with the lymph glands, the sufferer is not making up the symptoms, he is really feeling them. The headaches, for example are real, heart palpitations are easily detectable and the trembling of the hand can be seen by anyone.

- Chapter 3 -

WHAT ARE THE CAUSES OF HYPOCHONDRIA?

There are various theories as to how hypochondria develops. However, the exact cause is not yet clearly defined. In addition, it is often not clear whether hypochondria is a sickness in its own, or a symptom of another sickness. Someone, who suffers from depression, can develop hypochondria as a secondary indication. On the other hand, it is possible, that depression develops as a result of the hypochondria. In that case, it is difficult to decide whether the depression or the hypochondria is the sickness.

It is assumed, that hypochondria develops as a result of the interaction of several factors.

TRIGGER IN CHILDHOOD

It is probable, that particular experiences in childhood can trigger hypochondria, or at least it is assumed, that there is deep psychological explanation for it.

I am not going to go into detail about that in this book. If you are interested, there is a large amount of literature on the subject. Instead, I will give you short descriptions of the most common triggers on the following pages.

EXPERIENCE WITH SICKNESS AND DEATH

Often you can find a link to previous experiences in childhood, which are connected to the feared condition. In the case of a strong fear of cancer, for example, it is possible, that a person close to the sufferer, was suffering or indeed died from it. Being confronted with death can be formative and can change thought and behavioural patterns, which can lead to hypochondria in later life.

UNRESOLVED INNER CONFLICTS

If there are unresolved inner conflicts, these can lead to the mind influencing the body. The body, in turn, reacts to the situation. The psychological problems are transferred into physical ones, this is why hypochondria is referred to as a somatoform disorder, because there is no organic cause for the physically experienced symptoms.

Psychological problems manifest themselves in physical symptoms. This is why hypochondria is said to be a coping and self-healing strategy for other problems. It is assumed, that this transfer from mind to body happens in early childhood.

UPBRINGING BASED ON FEAR

The upbringing of a child and the behaviour of the parents can influence the development of hypochondria later in life. Parents who were too careful with their children, always worrying unnecessarily, that a child could be sick or hurt itself, end up restricting their child considerably. If that child experiences stress later in life, it can lead to an eventual development of a psychological sickness.

Those, who learned from a very early age to be careful, and to pay particular attention to their health, tend later to have far more physical pain and symptoms than those around them and have learned to give these signals significant value.

INFLUENCING FACTORS

The following factors can help to create hypochondria. It is not necessary for all the factors to appear. These are the most common influences found during a survey of those affected:

EXCESSIVE BELIEF IN AN EXISTING SICKNESS

One of the most important origins for the development of hypochondria is said to be excessive belief in the existence of a sickness. This causes an overestimation in the probability and severity of an existing sickness. An overblown interpretation of one's physical symptoms can be a deciding factor in the development of hypochondria.

LOW SELF-ESTEEM

Often, hypochondriacs have a lower self-esteem than other people and feel particularly vulnerable. Studies have shown that there is a connection between having a low self-esteem and hypochondria. Therefore, those people, who tend to have low self-confidence should beware of any hypochondriacal symptoms and actively work on improving their self-esteem.

DESIRE FOR ATTENTION

Hypochondriacs show an increased desire for attention and assistance. This can happen if they have previously experienced a lot more attention as a sick person than they otherwise would have.

The attention, that they initially get for their sickness, usually wanes increasingly as time goes on. After the first few times, that their suspicions have not been confirmed by the doctor, the people around them pay less and less attention to the symptoms. Sufferers often hear sentences like "I am sure it is nothing, last time the doctor said, you are healthy, do not worry".

It is possible, that the sufferer then turns to the internet instead of the people around him to get the attention he desires. The sufferer has a platform on internet forums, where many people can speak and exchange views and suggestions about their sicknesses.

EMOTIONAL INSTABILITY

By 'emotional stability', I mean when a person remains stable and well balanced. At the beginning of hypochondria, the opposite is often the case, and there is an underlying instability in his mental state, or 'Neuroticism', as it is known technically.

Neuroticism is often combined with:

- Insecurity

- Anxiety

- Inhibitions

- Mood swings

- Nervousness

- Vulnerability

If his emotional instability becomes strong, the sufferer becomes very sensitive and reacts very emotionally. Events, which other people would not normally worry about, can cause a hypochondriac to lose control. For example: While others can quietly read a newspaper, a hypochondriac can get very upset about a particular article. It becomes more difficult for him to control his stress levels than it is for other people and he is very quick to feel anxious or threatened.

EMOTIONAL BLINDNESS

Difficulty in cognitively processing emotions is known technically as Alexithymia. In everyday language, one speaks of emotional coldness.

In the past, Alexithymia was considered to be a perso-nality disorder, which also triggered psychosomatic symptoms. Today, this belief is disputed. It is more likely to be connected to a lack of emotional intelligence. By emotional intelligence, I mean, that a person is capable of recognising and classifying his own and other people's feelings, which is not the case here.

When a person is suffering from Alexithymia, it is not possible for him to recognise the feelings he or other people are experiencing, nor is he capable of expressing those feelings. This is why we speak of a lack of emotional intelligence.

About 10 percent of Germans suffer from emotional blindness. As about one in ten people are affected, it is possible that you know such a person or even suffer from it yourself. Alexithymia implies an inability to recognise or express your own feelings. This includes an inability to verbalise emotions.

The following can become difficult:

- Recognising and accepting your own emotions.
- Guiding and influencing your own feelings.
- Reacting appropriately to an emotional situation.
- Specifically using emotions in order to achieve a goal.
- Being able to put yourself in the place of others as far as their feelings are concerned.
- Understanding the emotional behaviour of others.

These deficiencies lead to many difficulties in everyday life. This, above all, affects your social competence because your inability to recognise the feelings of others also affects your social interactions.

It is important to note, that emotional blindness does not mean, that you do not have feelings, but that you do not recognise the feelings you have and cannot verbalise them.

STRESS

Stress, fundamental changes or radical events are often the precursors to hypochondria phases. Stress can cause physical symptoms, such as irregular heartbeat, dizziness, digestion problems or headaches. This is perfectly normal and can be directly attributable to the circumstances present at the time.

However, if a person attributes a certain meaning to these physical symptoms, during times of stress and caused by the stress itself, this can lead to misinterpretation of the causes and the person assumes, that he is suffering from a particular sickness.

This becomes a vicious circle: The stress causes the anxiety of becoming ill. The anxiety leads to an increase in the stress level, which in turn leads to more attention being paid to the assumed sickness. The sufferer then tries to find out more information through the internet or text books, which in turn confirms his fears, that he has that particular sickness. The symptoms continue to worsen, which increases the anxiety of having a serious illness and the stress level rises once more.

In my case the stress at work caused me to have headaches. I interpreted these symptoms to be a brain tumour. In the internet I found confirmation of my hypothesis. That caused even more stress, and in turn, more headaches. That made me feel vindicated in my assumption, that I was sick. This is how I found myself in the vicious circle, one which I was completely caught up in. I did not realise, that it was really the stress, that had caused the headaches, probably tension headaches, a very common event.

DYSFUNCTIONAL PERSONAL DEFENCE MECHANISM

We know, that racing at 180 km/h down the motorway increases the risk of having an accident and that smoking can cause lung cancer. We know that and yet many people still do it. Why? Because we usually think, that it will not happen to us. It is a kind of personal defence mechanism. This mechanism is not working properly in people, who are hypochondriacs. In their cases, the dangers, which we are aware of, become substantial threats. These changes in our own perceptions are often the cause of the hypo-chondriacal symptoms and other psychological sicknesses, as a large number of studies have shown.

MEDIA

The media creates a great danger for hypochondriacal anxiety to begin, or in strengthening already existing hypochondriacal tendencies. Health and doctor series are an integral part of the daily menu on TV. Internet also offers an enormous range of information, which is often too great to digest.

Health management is a highly regarded subject in the media. How can we recognise a sickness in its early stages? TV, magazines and the internet provide many suggestions. Today, it is the internet, which is mostly used to find information. This can cause and strengthen fear of a sickness in many ways. Therein lies the danger of developing hypochondriacal behaviour.

In addition, beginners are taught to test themselves. It is all well and good for healthy people to carry out a certain amount of self-testing as a prophylactic for sickness, but for a hypochondriac, such tests usually do more harm than good.

PERSONAL EXPERIENCE OF A SICKNESS

Early experiences of sickness can play a role in the development of hypochondria. If someone has had a negative experience in the past, such as knowing someone, who had a sickness, which was detected too late or someone whose symptoms were not taken seriously enough, the fear of having an illness increases because a lack of trust develops towards the doctors. If this leads to a basic mistrust of the whole medical scene, this can quickly cause hypochondriacal signs, because doctors are unable to refute the symptoms and the patient is unable to accept explanations given by the doctors.

GENETIC FACTORS

You are not born a hypochondriac. However, genetic factors can have a certain influence in the generation of anxiety. If someone is born with a genetic predisposition for anxiety, that person is more likely to be at risk of anxiety-related conditions. Nevertheless, genetically influenced factors do not play a great role in the development of hypochondria. The reason is much more likely to be outside influences or personal experiences of individuals.

- Chapter 4 -

HOW DO YOU RECOGNISE HYPOCHONDRIA?

It could be a long time before the hypochondria of an individual is recognised. It is particularly difficult if you, as the affected person, do not realise, that you are not physically sick.

The first helping hand generally comes from the general practitioner (GP). He is normally the person you would go to first. He often has knowledge of your medical history and is able to explain the results of any examinations you may have had. He is the best person to recognise, if any real health risks are present and if you arc being over-anxious about them.

If the GP suspects hypochondria, he will begin by speaking to you about it and perhaps will follow it up with a therapy by a psychiatrist or psychologist. For this, you would have to give your permission, which means, that you have to be able to recognise, that there is something wrong.

Before psychotherapy can begin, you need to have certainty, that you are not suffering from a medical condition. This would involve a series of tests and examinations.

EXAMINATIONS BY THE PSYCHIATRIST OR PSYCHOLOGIST

During the first appointment with a psychiatrist or psychologist, he will make a thorough analysis, based on certain points, which you have discussed with him.

Modern tests are used to make a diagnosis. These are usually questionnaires, which the psychiatrist or psychologist can determine whether hypochondria is present and if yes, how pronounced it is.

The questions would be similar to those in our self-test, but for the diagnosis, they will be more specific.

CRITERIA FOR THE DIAGNOSIS

Hypochondria is recognised by the World Health Organisation as an independent sickness. One speaks of hypochondria, if the sufferer constantly and excessively worries about becoming or being sick.

It is important to distinguish between a temporary fear of becoming sick and an excessive anxiety. In order to diagnose hypochondria, the following criteria from the American Diagnosis Catalogue (DSM-V) must be met:

- Excessive worry about becoming or being sick.

- Physical symptoms are not present, or are only present in a mild form. If there are serious symptoms, it is a matter of discretion as to whether the worry is excessive or not.

- The sufferer has a high anxiety level for sickness and is easily worried by health problems.

- Excessive behaviour towards his health or avoidance of speaking about health sub-jects.

- The anxiety must have been in existence for at least six months. The feared sickness does not need to be the same one.

- Medical examinations have given negative results. There is no better explanation for the symptoms than hypochondria and above all, no anxiety or panic disorders are present.

TWO DIVISIONS

In general, there are two types of hypochondria: One group of hypochondriacs wants their symptoms to be looked at often and therefore often seeks medical assistance, such as going to the doctor or specialist, and allows technical information to be gathered, such as X-ray or Computer Tomography scans. The other group avoids going to the doctor completely, because the fear is too great, that the suspected diagnosis would be confirmed.

The American classification system for psychological disorders divides hypochondria in a different way. There is the group of hypochondriacs, who complain of physical symptoms and those, who suffer more from anxiety.

Both types of division are very similar. In both there is a group, which worries about physical symptoms and wants to speak about them with a doctor. The other group is the "silent" group, which is just as worried about the symptoms, but has more fear of knowing, that the sickness exists, and therefore avoids seeking medical help.

DISTINCTION FROM OTHER SICKNESSES

While making the diagnosis, it can be difficult to ascertain whether it is really hypochondria or something else. There are some criteria, which the doctor can use to distinguish between hypochondria and other sicknesses.

Those sicknesses, which are often confused with hypochondria but need a different therapy, are briefly mentioned and explained in the next chapter. It is not possible to give more detail on other sicknesses in this book, because we are concentrating here only on hypochondria. However, there is a lot of interesting literature, about those other sicknesses, which goes into further detail about the individual diagnoses.

MILD HYPOCHONDRIACAL WORRIES

According to the diagnosis criteria, hypochondria has to have existed for at least six months. This is not the case by mild hypochondriacal worries. These can occur over a shorter period of time and cause much less impact on the daily life of the sufferer. When we speak of a short-term occurrence of the symptoms, we do not speak of hypochondria but of mild hypo-chondriacal worries, which are much easier to treat.

SOMATOFORM DISORDERS

Contrary to hypochondriacs, someone who suffers from a somatoform disorder displays distinct physical symptoms. Hypochondria presents more as a fear or conviction, that the patient is suffering from a serious illness, rather than a specific symptom. Although these symptoms are not due to any organic sickness, they are experienced much more strongly by patients, than those suffering from hypochondria.

DELUSIONAL DISORDERS

A true delusional disorder is different from hypo-chondria in that no matter how many examinations you have, you cannot be dissuaded from your belief. You are 100% sure of being sick and you will not budge. If you are a hypochondriac, you can, at least for a short time, be persuaded, that there are no negative results from your examinations. If you are delusional, this is no longer possible. Delusional disorder is a progression from hypochondria.

PANIC DISORDER

A panic disorder is focused on a particular physical event, such as a heart attack or heart failure. This is less about fear of a sickness. Here you have fear of having more panic attacks. The panic attack is much more acute but does not last very long. However, they can keep coming back and can happen often. As the name says, this disorder is accompanied by acute panic and fear of losing one's life.

GENERAL FEAR DISORDER

General fear disorder includes fear of being seriously ill. However, this is not the primary cause of the fear. This is one of many fears the sufferer has. You could say it is a generic term for fear disorders, where hypochondria is only a small part.

ILLNESS PHOBIA

Illness phobia is similar to the fear of having an illness. The difference is that, with illness phobia, it is a general fear of becoming ill, whether or not you are sure that you have any sickness. There is less emphasis on the symptoms but more on the requirement to stay healthy, which can turn into a pathological behaviour pattern. As an example, it could be the compulsion to wash your hands in order to stay free of bacteria and viruses.

COMPULSIVE DISORDER

Similar symptoms are to be found be a compulsive disorder. As with the fear of sickness, the compulsive disorder sufferer feels the need, as does the hypochondriac, to behave in a way that he does not become sick in the first place. He develops compulsive rituals to avoid sicknesses, which is where this disorder differs from hypochondria.

ORGANIC SICKNESS

By physical (i.e. organic) sicknesses, the sufferer is afraid of having a sickness, which is then confirmed by tests and examinations. In this case, the sufferer is really suffering from that sickness and is not imagining it. This is basically 'normal'. The sickness is not imagined but exists in reality.

FEAR OF PROGRESSION

The fear of progression (FOP) is the fear, which is experienced regarding the progression of a particular sickness with all its negative consequences. The difference between FOP and hypochondria is that the physical sickness is real and at an early stage or only mildly experienced. This condition is suffered mostly by those with chronic sicknesses and who worry about the progression of the symptoms.

COMMON COMORBIDITIES (ACCOMPANYING ILLNESSES)

The distinction between sicknesses is not always simple because the hypochondria is often accompanied by additional illnesses. The primary sickness needs to be found first before treating the accompanying problems. In the following pages, I will briefly introduce the most frequent accompanying illnesses which are found with hypochondria:

DEPRESSION

Depression is the most common accompanying sickness of hypochondria. About 40% to 50% of all hypochondriacs suffer simultaneously from depression. However, the hypochondria usually forms before the depression, which leads us to believe, that a hypochondriac has a much greater risk of developing a depression.

ANXIETY DISORDERS

The second most common accompanying sickness is the anxiety disorder, particularly panic attacks with Claustrophobia. These make up about a third of all accompanying sicknesses. Anxiety disorders usually appear at the same time as or shortly before the hypochondria. Hypochondria can develop from an anxiety attack and can run parallel to it.

SOMATOFORM DISORDERS

Although somatoform disorders appear quite often, there is little information about them because hypochondria is considered to be a subordinate form of a somatoform disorder. When described in the previous pages, I have counted the somatoform disorder as a separate illness from hypochondria. Studies suggest, that roughly between 7% and 21% of all hypochondriacs additionally suffer from a somatoform disorder.

- Chapter 5 -

EFFECTS OF HYPOCHONDRIA

The hypochondriacal disorder impacts greatly on ourselves and our social environment. Mostly, we do not suffer alone, our close companions and family usually suffer too.

PERSONAL EFFECTS

Hypochondria changes people. If you were once a lively and happy person, it could be, that you are now gloomy, dejected and you wander through life, lost in your own thoughts.

The people you work with notice, that you are taking more days off sick and when you are there, you appear inattentive. Being lost in your thoughts is taking a lot of your time and often prevents you from focusing on your work.

Also, in your private life, the hypochondria is taking its toll on your free time activities and hobbies. Particularly sporting activities are being neglected because you want to protect your body, which you believe is sick.

PHYSICAL EFFECTS

Hypochondria usually causes psychological symptoms but it can also lead to physical complaints and complications. For example, stress can cause you to break out in sweats, heart palpitations or even panic attacks.

Often, many medicines are taken, which are not necessary because there is no underlying sickness. These medicines have side-effects and can cause harm to your organs.

SOCIAL IMPACT

The most notable effect of hypochondria is to be seen in the social impact. You are so fixated on yourself and withdrawn into your own thoughts and fears that you become less connected to your social contacts.

Alternatively, it can lead to you directly avoiding your close contacts. This can happen, if you do not feel that people care when you speak about the physical symptoms, which are bothering you. You do not feel as if you are being taken seriously and so you avoid these people.

The social isolation become stronger, the longer you are suffering from the hypochondria. This increases the danger, that you sink further into your own world and depressions appear out of the isolation.

For our loved ones it is very difficult to deal with a sickness, which is not there. They often do not know how best to support you and what you really need. However, these loved ones are the most important support you can have in your life.

- Chapter 6 -

TREATMENT OF HYPOCHONDRIA

Not every hypochondriac needs therapy. You can treat light or non-chronic forms by yourself. Particularly when the symptoms and fears have not been present for more than 6 months, there is a good chance, that you can help yourself back to wellness. Please see the next chapter regarding this.

When the problems have existed for more than half a year, when doctors or psychotherapists are unable to reassure you and you feel, that your lifestyle is being restricted, this could be a sign that you need professional support.

Unprocessed, dramatic or traumatic experiences can be the cause of hypochondria. Professional support could be necessary to help you get through them.

The professional therapy plan for hypochondria consists mainly of psychotherapy. The cognitive behavioural approach seems to be the most used. This form of psychotherapy is also used for anxicty disorders. Only the most difficult cases of hypo-chondria are treated using medication.

As the comorbidity, with depression, anxiety, panic attacks, compulsive and somatisation disorder is high, the secondary diseases should also be treated at the same time.

COGNITIVE BEHAVIOURAL PSYCHOTHERAPY

As in cases of anxiety disorder, cognitive behavioural therapy is the most common form of therapy. Its aim is, on the one side, to change thought patterns (cognitive) and, on the other side, to change behaviour.

In the cognitive part, the aim is to reduce the overestimated belief, on the part of the client, that an illness is probable. Behaviour, such as constant observation of symptoms and regular doctor visits needs to change.

An important part of the therapy is to show the client, which body functions and sensations are perfectly normal, present in every person, and nothing to worry about. These include, for example, heartbeat, sweating or bowel movements.

In addition, the client is shown what physical symptoms, like stress and fear, can cause in the body, which are often misinterpreted.

There are supporting experiments, which can be carried out, so that you can see how your body reacts to drinking several cups of coffee, for example, or to sleep deprivation. Finally, you will be shown how to evaluate realistically whether or not you are seriously ill.

You will be given several behavioural exercises where you can learn how to change your behaviour. Various techniques can be used here, such as the paradox intensification of behaviour, the making of reports, reducing doctor visits and reducing other self-assurance measures you normally take, such as speaking to relatives or looking in the media.

PSYCHOTHERAPY

With psychotherapy, you will learn to trust your own body more and to reduce the fears. According to studies, cognitive behavioural therapy, together with confrontational therapy – where the client has to face his fears in order to gain control over them – has the best chance of success. With hypochondriacs, this therapy is carried out predominantly in psychosomatic clinics, which are specialised in the treatment of health anxiety.

PSYCHO-SENSORY PROCEDURES

Psycho-sensory techniques are used with increasing success in the treatment of anxiety, including the fear of sickness. The client is led into a world of light, colour, music and warmth, leading to deeper relaxation, and a feeling of security and harmony. The best-known psycho-sensory techniques are EMDR from Dr. Francine Shapiro, TFT from Dr. Roger Callahan, EFT from Gary Craig, OEI from Dr. Rick Bradshaw and colleagues, and 'Havening' from Dr. Ronald A. Ruden. I do not want to delve too deeply into the various psycho-sensory techniques in this book. If you are interested in this subject, I would suggest reading the technical literature, which is available on the market.

MEDICINAL THERAPY

There are very few studies regarding the effectiveness of medicinal therapy for hypochondria. The most common medication used is that, which is often used for other psychiatric conditions, the so-called selective serotonin reuptake inhibitor (SSRI).

Serotonin is an important neurotransmitter in the brain. The aim is to improve the symptoms of the hypochondria by administering SSRIs. However, there have not yet been any studies, which prove that the improvement of the symptoms remains stable after the patients have discontinued the medicine.

Hypochondria is often accompanied by other disorders. In the case of a hypochondria with accompanying depression, anti-depressives could help here.

In cases of severe schizophrenic symptoms, such as hypochondriacal delusion, nerve suppression remedies – so called neuroleptics – are prescribed.

PROGRESSION AND PROGNOSIS IN HYPOCHONDRIA

The hypochondriacal disorder is considered to be incurable, but with timely treatment in the form of self-help or professional help, the chances, that you will get back your quality of life are good.

Psychosocial stress, sicknesses among close associates or life-changing experiences can trigger the occurrence of hypochondria and relapses are possible. The most important thing is, that you recognise that it is only fear which causes the symptoms and not a real illness.

If, through cognitive behavioural therapy or self-help, you have learned to guide your thought processes away from these fears, you can begin to use these techniques once again.

It is also important, that any accompanying disorders, such as depression or anxiety, are treated at the same time as the hypochondria in order to achieve the best therapy results.

- Chapter 7 -

LIBERATE YOURSELF FROM YOUR FEARS IN FOUR STAGES

Hypochondria can be conquered, but it can take time while you are working on yourself. You alone hold the key to success and you just need to learn what you have to do to enjoy a carefree life once again.

I will show you, step by step, how I freed myself from my hypochondriacal disorder. Today I feel very well and I would like to make that possible for you by sharing with you the self-developed concept, which gave me my life back.

This procedure helped me and I am sure that many other people can also profit from it. Please remember, that if you are not successful in dealing with your symptoms, despite trying out everything you can, I suggest emphatically, that you find an expert to help you.

I cannot promise immediate healing. It is my aim to show you a way, step by step, how to work on yourself and your fears in order to reduce them. I cannot give you a guarantee of success, but I can encourage you to take this opportunity to give it a try. After all, you have nothing to lose and much to gain.

STEP 1: OBSERVATION

To start with, you should observe your behaviour in the next 7 days. You should be looking at how often you are preoccupied with your body.

Writing down my observations, it became clear to me, that I was spending most of the day being preoccupied with my body. Time which I could be putting to better use if I had been free of these fears.

DIARY

Try to write a diary over a period of 7 days. Account for every time you notice a symptom or fear. Every time, that you think about a sickness or symptom, note it down, including the time of the occurrence. This also includes the time you spend on the internet or in text books, looking into your symptoms. Make a note of the time taken for your searches.

From my experience, this can become a long list but it does not matter at all. On the contrary, the longer the list, the quicker you will realise how much this deviates from normal behaviour and how much you want to change this.

STEP 2: INSIGHT

Through your observations, did you notice that your thoughts and behaviour take up a great deal of your day? Then I hope you are ready for the next and most important step.

The second step is not only the most important, it is also the most difficult. If you have lived in the belief, that you have a serious illness for a long time, it is not easy to get rid of that and to accept, that you are not physically ill.

MEDICAL CONSULTATION

It could help you to confirm definitively that you are not physically ill by visiting your family doctor. Speak with him about your emotions and what this step feels like. Perhaps you need a further blood test or examination for you to accept, that the sickness you are suffering from does not exist. This is OK as long as you do this in the hope, that you can convince yourself you are healthy. It would not be helpful for you to provoke further upset and doubt.

The visit to the doctor is also useful so that you know, that there is an expert at your side to help you, while you are trying to heal yourself. Regular visits, planned in advance, to review your progress, can also be helpful. Your doctor is more likely to recognise if you are losing your way and giving in to your fears again.

DIAGNOSTIC FINDINGS IN BLACK AND WHITE

It could help you to have a print out of the results of your blood tests or other examinations or results, of which there are most probably many from the past. You have the right to demand all your results.

Look at the results in black and white, probably written by various doctors. That helped me to see, that my suspicions of the diagnosis had not been confirmed and the sickness did not exist.

TALK TO RELATIVES

Talk to your close relatives. It could help you to speak about the feelings which caused you to feel that way, but also to hear their opinions about you.

It was very important for me to include my closest confidants in the process. They had also been suffering in some way during the time I believed myself to be sick. My desperation did not go unnoticed.

My relatives were relieved, that I had gained some insight into my problem and I was able to include them in supporting me with the process. We became closer again because we were all pursuing the same aim. My relationships with my relatives were sometimes difficult during my hypochondriacal phases because they did not feel the same way as me, and did not take my supposed illnesses seriously. You probably recognise this feeling yourself. This is why I want to encourage you to speak to your closest confidants. Take them with you on your journey and fight your fears together with them. With this social network behind you, you have support which is important during the process of freeing yourself from your hypochondriacal disorder.

STEP 3: MIND CONTROL

In Step 1, you noted your observations regarding your thoughts about possible sicknesses and your anxiety. Step 3 is about learning to control and manage these fears when they arise.

Stop rising anxiety and thoughts about your body by saying "Stop" to yourself and not allowing the thought to continue. With the word "stop", you should also stop your internet search or your intention to go to the doctor.

POSITIVE AFFIRMATION

Positive affirmation is an effective technique by which you can combat your fears or anxiety. With it you can manage your thought processes and change and improve them.

Affirmations are short, positive statements, that help you to achieve what you want to achieve. They can be used in all situations. We use them to break through our thought patterns.

That seems a simple matter at first. The difficult part is to create sentences, which you feel make sense to you. It depends on what you think and feel. Being able to put that all into one sentence can change your subconscious and your thought processes in the long term.

Write a positive affirmation on a Post-it or a scrap of paper. Avoid negative words in your sentence, such as "not" or "none", because these can be subconsciously filtered out of your brain and the sentence can have the opposite effect. An example is a sentence, such as "I am not afraid". It would be better to formulate it, so that it reads "I am free from anxiety, fearless and self-confident".

The following sentences are those which I formulated and used. These are meant to be examples. It is better for you to make your own personal sentences which you can say with conviction:

- "I am feeling better and better about my body, every day."

- "My body is healthy and resilient."

- "I am feeling a little bit better every day."

- "I love the feeling of being able to make decisions about my own life."

You need to develop a feeling for every affirmation. You should feel a connection to them so that you do not just say the words but that they reach your subconscious.

No one is born a master. Practising the positive affirmations took me a few days to get used to. I recommend standing in front of a mirror and looking into your own eyes, when you say the sentences. Speak directly to yourself! This may seem a little strange at the beginning so it will take a while before you feel comfortable with this technique.

There are various ways to use your affirmations. For example:

- You say them loud to your mirror image and look yourself in the eyes.

- You think of them.

- You say them out loud to yourself.

- You repeat them every time you get up or go to bed.

- You write them out again every day.

- You write them onto a Post-it or a scrap of paper and hang them around your home.

- You sing them to yourself.

- You let them appear every day on your calendar, computer or mobile phone.

- You play them to yourself on a pre-recorded audio recording, a sort of recorded message.

My sentences helped me, on the one hand, to strengthen my thoughts and, on the other hand, I used them as a technique if I was suffering from a physical symptom, such as a headache. In such cases, I spoke the sentences either to myself or out loud, depending on the situation:

"I am feeling better and better about my body, every day. My body is healthy and resilient. I am feeling a little bit better every day. I love the feeling of being able to make decisions about my own life."

Using the affirmations, I can drive away the negative thoughts before they start to control me. I am saying "stop" to the negative patterns of thought that I had before and guiding myself towards positive thoughts.

These sentences accompany me every day, even if I am feeling good, they stay with me and they strengthen me.

STEP 4: STABILISATION

For the 4th step you are now able to manage your thoughts and to cast out negative thoughts. You recognise, if danger is approaching, which could lead you back into your old thought patterns. Your affirmations help you to combat them and maintain your convictions.

You are on the right path! Say that to yourself again and again. Keep thinking about your affirmations. In this phase it is enough to do that once a day. The important thing is, that you always feel a connection to those sentences.

In this phase, it is important to gain stability and peace, to remain strong and not to fall back into your old habits. Sport or other physical activities can help you with this, as can relaxation techniques. I will be providing various relaxation techniques in the next chapter.

SPORT AND PHYSICAL ACTIVITY

Many people underestimate the importance of sport and other physical activity. As a hypochondriac, you will tend to be overprotective towards your body, due to your fear of becoming ill. As a consequence, your stamina worsens and causes you to feel more physical symptoms, resulting from your lack of condition.

Start your physical activity or sport today and integrate it into your normal life so that you feel more vitality. Do not overdo it. The best way is to start slowly but stay focused. Try to do some form of physical activity every second day. Decide what type of activity you enjoy most. Ball sport? Do you like to dance? Is Zumba something for you? There are thousands of ways to be active. The most important thing is, that you find something you like to do.

I love nature and I started to ride my bike at least 3 or 4 times a week, irrespective of the weather. I started with short distances and over time I have noticed how my stamina has improved, allowing me to cover ever longer distances. This helps me to feel positive about myself and to be fit and full of vitality. Sometimes, it helps me to manage oncoming anxiety by saying my affirmations with every push of the pedal until my head clears again.

In order to improve my condition and muscles, I do strengthening exercises at home, using my own body, known as bodyweight training. I bought myself some exercise DVDs especially for this. I do not like going into fitness centres very much so I decided to find a training programme, which I can carry out spontaneously, wherever I am.

There are so many possibilities. At the beginning you will need to have a lot of discipline to overcome your weaker self, but when the physical activity becomes part of your everyday life, you will see that you will not want to be without it anymore, because it makes you feel so much better.

YOGA AND MEDITATION

Yoga is an ancient Indian philosophical teaching, which has the unification of body, mind and soul at its heart. Those, who practise yoga, in the western world, usually carry out physical exercises (Asanas) and breathing exercises (Pranayama). The main aim of yoga is to achieve "liberating redemption".

The main difference between yoga and normal gymnastics is the maintenance of inner posture and a focus on breathing. There is always a connection between the breathing technique and the focus on our inner selves. In the exercise forms, specific instructions are given when to breathe in and out. The heart beats faster when you breathe in and breathing out causes the pulse to slow down. This is how you can influence your nervous system and control your muscles and organs.

Yoga stimulates the metabolism and strengthens the nervous system. In addition, the breathing exercises help to reduce tension and stress.

These days, yoga and meditation are generally seen as methods to gain or keep good health and as a way to reduce tension.

For me, yoga is a wonderful method to balance body and mind. The "sun salutation" has become an integral part of my everyday life and I always start my day with it. On those days when I have planned less physical activity, I tend to extend my yoga practice time.

Try to start with simple exercises at first, if you have not had any experience with yoga, or you can enrol with a yoga group close to your home.

RELAXATION TECHNIQUES

In addition to physical activity, I recommend learning relaxation techniques and using them regularly. Hypochondriacs tend to go through life in a tense and obsessive way and their mind does not come to rest.

In order to get some distance between you and your negative thoughts, relaxation techniques, such as progressive muscle relation or autogenic training, can help.

Find out, which relaxation technique you prefer and use it regularly. This will help you to find inner peace and generally you will feel more in balance.

Both of the relaxation techniques mentioned above are described in detail in the following chapter, together with instructions on how to do them.

- Chapter 8 -

RELAXATION TECHNIQUES WITH INSTRUCTIONS

In our society, the need for inner balance is growing. We are looking for inner peace in our stressful everyday life and at work. An increasing number of people are using relaxation techniques, which are not only useful in supporting therapies, but are also recommended for anyone to do.

Four techniques, which I find very good for achieving relaxation and releasing anxiety, compulsions and worries are: Progressive muscle relaxation, autogenic training, yoga and meditation.

Below I will introduce you to the two relaxation techniques - progressive muscle relaxation and auto-genic training – because I think they are less well known than, for example, yoga.

PROGRESSIVE MUSCLE RELAXATION

Progressive muscle relaxation, or PMR for short, was developed in the early 1920s by the American psychologist Edmund Jacobson. It is often called PMR according to Jacobson. He was looking for exercises, which could relieve him from his own back pain, which had been caused by spending a lot of time sitting down. While carrying out his relaxation exercises, he noticed, that it was not only his muscles, which relaxed, but also his mind became more peaceful. He assumed, that muscle tension was always connected to excitement or anxiety. Or, to put it another way, anxiety, stress and psychological stress could also be reduced by reducing muscle tension.

The technique is very easy to learn and is therefore suitable for almost everyone. You do not need special equipment or any particular training plan. The technique can be performed almost anywhere.

During specific incidents or situations, which cause stress, for example before an examination, on an aeroplane etc., you can carry out short sequences of

PMR unnoticed and this way you can achieve swift relief from stress or tension.

AIM

The main aim of this method is to develop a so-called "muscular sense" by training your body to achieve a better self-awareness.

The second focus lies on the reduction of anxiety. PMR should reduce emotional tension and stress. Carrying out the exercises regularly, should lead to a reduction in the psychosomatic symptoms of tension, such as headaches, tremors, nervousness or palpitations.

APPLICATIONS

PMR is often used in combination with behavioural therapy. It has been very successful in dealing with anxiety or borderline disorders. It is also useful as an accompanying treatment for high blood pressure, headaches, chronic backache, sleeping disorders and stress.

CONTRAINDICATIONS

PMR is not recommended for treating schizophrenic psychosis or by people who have compulsive tendencies. In such cases, it could prove to have the opposite effect. PMR is often discouraged in cases of hypochondria because it causes the sufferer to concentrate even more on his own body.

I recommend PMR for hypochondria only in the 4th phase, the phase of stabilisation.

THE 2 AREAS OF PMR

The physical side:

In this exercise, the most important muscle groups are tensed up, under instruction, for between 5 – 7 seconds each, in a pre-determined order. The tension is suddenly released and the participant feels the effect of the resulting relaxation.

The eyes remain closed throughout the exercise, so that there are no visual distractions. This way, you can concentrate completely on your own awareness and feel the difference between tension and relaxation.

Above all, the feeling of relaxing the muscle is of great significance. The feeling of relaxation which occurs can be sensed directly at the physical level. Contrary to having a relaxed mind, under these circumstances, the body relaxation can be felt directly in the muscle.

The more motivated you are at the beginning, the more you risk tensing your muscles too much. This can lead to cramps or muscle stiffness the next day. Therefore, it is recommended, that you only tense the muscle up to 80% of the maximum. That is just under the maximum, but do not go above this.

The mental side of PMR:

The mental side of PMR differs from the physical side as it does not concentrate on the tension and relaxation of the muscles. It is more about feeling the difference between them.

Advanced proponents of PMR do not necessarily have to physically carry out the exercise, they can follow them mentally, similarly to autogenic training, based on listening in to the body. The person imagines how his muscle tension releases so that the muscle groups can relax. Experienced people can reach a deep stage of relaxation, in a very short time, with this mental technique.

The mental form of this exercise needs a lot of practice and long-term experience with PMR. I am still learning. I am still not very successful with the mental form. I notice the effectiveness and relaxation much more using the physical form, but this does not mean, that I will not be able to use the mental form effectively one day.

INSTRUCTIONS

Duration:

You will need about 15 to 30 minutes for this exercise.

Preparation:

Choose a quiet place where you will not be disturbed. You can carry out this exercise sitting or lying down. If possible, dim the lights a little.

Lie on your back and relax. You can lay your head on a blanket if you like and place one or two cushions under your knee joints, if you need them.

Place your legs slightly apart, your arms away from your body, palms facing upwards, shoulders away from your ears and stretch your neck long.

Implementation:

Now we will concentrate on the individual body parts in the following five steps:

- First locate the body part to be worked on,

- Tighten the muscles in the body part,

- Hold the tension,

- Release the tension slowly,

- Feel the relaxation in the muscle.

Hands and arms:

Feel the right hand. Tense the right hand and the forearm slowly, make a fist and tense the forearm. Make a very strong fist, feel the tension in the muscles. Now hold the tension, notice how the forearm and right-hand feel. Now slowly release the tension and feel the relaxation in the forearm and fingers.

Feel the left hand. Tense the left hand and the forearm slowly, make a fist and tense the forearm. Make a very strong fist, feel the tension in the muscles. Now hold the tension, notice how the tension in the forearm and left-hand feel. Now slowly release the tension and feel the relaxation in the forearm and fingers.

Feel the right arm, from the fingers to the shoulder, and tense the whole arm. Make a fist again and press the lower arm into the ground and feel the tension in the arm. Hold the tension and notice how it feels, then slowly relax the arm. Feel the relaxation in the arm muscles.

Feel the left arm, from the fingers to the shoulder and tense the whole arm. Make a fist again and press the lower arm into the ground and feel the tension in the arm. Hold the tension and notice how it feels, then slowly relax the arm. Feel the relaxation in the arm muscles.

Face and head:
Feel your face from the chin to the forehead and up to the crown. Tense the face muscles by contracting all the muscles up to the tip of your nose, including the eyebrows; furrow the brows and forehead and contract your cheek muscles up to the tip of your nose. Feel the tension then slowly release it, feeling the relaxation of the face muscles as you go.

Feel the throat and neck. Pull the chin down towards the chest and press the back of your head gently into the ground or cushion. Feel the tension in the neck, slowly release it and feel the relaxation in your neck muscles.

Torso:
Feel your whole back and torso, from the buttocks, lower back, mid back and upper back. Pull your shoulder blades together, tense the stomach and buttock muscles. Feel the tension in your torso and

hold on to it. Feel the tension then slowly release it. Feel the relaxation in the muscles of your torso.

Legs and feet:
Feel the right leg from the toes, through your calves to your thighs. Pull your toes upwards towards your head and increase the tension in your leg. Press your heels into the ground, tense the muscles of the right leg. Feel the tension then slowly release it. Feel the relaxation in the muscles of your right leg.

Feel the left leg from the toes, through your calves to your thighs. Pull your toes upwards towards your head and increase the tension in your leg. Press your heels into the ground, tense the muscles of the left leg. Feel the tension of your left leg then slowly release it. Feel the relaxation in the muscles of your left leg.

Enjoy this wonderful feeling of relaxation in your whole body. Feel the relaxation again in all the muscle groups, one at a time, starting with the feet right up to the muscles in your head. Enjoy the feeling of being relaxed for a few minutes in silence.

This is where we begin to close the exercise and to relax. Now you can say an affirmation, such as "I feel wide awake, peaceful and refreshed". It is something, that you can say at this moment with conviction while you finish the exercise.

AUTOGENIC TRAINING

Autogenic training is a relaxation technique based on auto-suggestion. The psychiatrist Johannes Heinrich Schultz from Berlin developed the concept from the practice of hypnosis and first introduced it in 1926. Schulz's relaxation technique is a modified method of hypnosis, which works with the help of a person's own imagination, in order to reach a state of relaxation but without reaching such deep changes of consciousness as with hypnosis. He once described his autogenic technique as "Yoga of the west".

In comparison with yoga and other forms of meditations, you do not work with tension and relaxation, in fact it is almost completely void of physical activity. Instead the focus is on easy auto-suggestive exercises, which result in a deep state of relaxation.

When practising autogenic training you can reach a state of relaxation, where you can strongly influence your physical and mental state. For example, it can lead to an end of compulsive behaviour, or simply reduce stress or to enable you to master your working life.

Anyone can learn autogenic training. It is up to you whether you prefer to learn it using a professional trainer, a CD or video, or learn it completely by yourself. You can find a whole range of video clips where you can learn autogenic training step by step. Try it out. You cannot really do anything wrong.

Aim
It is a whole-body method with the aim of returning the natural balance of body, spirit and soul. Basically, its aim is to focus your thoughts on reaching physical as well as mental relaxation in a state of tranquillity.

During autogenic training, you should concentrate completely on yourself and direct your attention inwards. The aim is to arrive at the "here and now" and not to allow yourself to be distracted by the outside world.

Applications
Autogenic training can help almost anyone to enjoy more quality of life and better health. For example, the mental training is ideal for achieving better per-formance at work or in sport, to be able to learn or sleep better.

Autogenic training can also be very helpful in combatting addictions, such as smoking, alcohol or other addictive substances.

Often, autogenic training is used as a self-help instrument, which can be used in many different life situations. It has a reassuring effect when dealing with a whole range of ailments. Examples of these are set out below:

- Hypertension

- Sleep disorders

- Pain, for example headaches, migraines, chronic pain

- Tinnitus

- Irritable bowel syndrome

- Metabolic disorders

- Bronchial asthma

- Libido disorders

- Eating disorders, such as overweight or underweight

- Cardio-vascular disorders

- Nervous irritability

- Insecurity

- Agitation

- Anxiety states

- Depression

- Inferiority complexes

- Exam nerves

- Problems with concentration

CONTRAINDICATIONS

Autogenic training is not recommended by disorders of the central nervous system or mental handicap.

In the case of psychiatric disorders, including hypochondria, it is advisable to consult your therapist prior to beginning autogenic training.

Similar to progressive muscle relaxation, I recommend autogenic training only in Step 4, the phase of stabilisation.

Autogenic training is separated into three steps. The first step is most suitable for beginners and is also the prerequisite for starting the next step. The following steps each increase in their intensity:

The Basic Step:
The techniques in the first step are directed towards the vegetative nervous system, specific muscle groups and the whole cardiovascular system. This step contains a complete programme for physical re-laxation, which is particularly suitable for beginners. Soon, I will be going into more detail about this.

The Intermediate Step:
This stage is for more advanced participants. It involves empowering the exercises, which were learned in the first step by stating your own (or given) formulae. This step concentrates particularly on emotional and social factors, because it is dealing with changes in behaviour or attitude.

The Advanced Step:
This step is for those, who have been focussing intensively on autogenic training and who have already

learned steps 1 and 2. The methods, which are used in the advanced step, are directed towards personal experiences or self-discovery. Using formulistic resolution development, it is possible to reach deeper into the sub-conscious. That could cause outbursts of emotions or experiences, which had not surfaced up to that point.

THE 7 BASIC FORMULAE

1. *Calmness Formula:*
"I am completely calm; nothing can disturb me."

The calmness exercise is the introductory phase. It serves to soothe and increase concentration. Close your eyes and try to imagine the sentence before your eyes.

2. *The Heaviness Formula*
"My arms and legs are very heavy."

The heaviness exercise should cause you to have a heavy feeling in the required places and can be brought about by continuous repetition of the formula in your head.

3. *The Warmth Formula*
"My arms and legs are warm."

This sentence should stimulate the blood circulation in those particular limbs.

4. *The Breathing Formula*
"My breath is calm and steady."

With this exercise, a sense of relaxation should occur, using focused breathing. Read the formula from your inner eye. Caution: Make sure you are not holding your breath; you should allow the breath to flow with the rhythm of your body. You will see how quickly your breath calms down by itself.

5. *The Heart Formula*
"My heartbeat is calm and steady."

During this exercise, you should direct your full concentration on your heartbeat.

6. *The Solar Plexus Formula*
"My torso is flowingly warm."

Concentrate intensively on the centre of your abdomen.

7. *The Head Formula*
"My head is clear; my forehead is cool."

This formula will help you to stay awake or to wake up and concentrate better.

INSTRUCTIONS

It usually takes a few weeks to learn the individual exercises. To begin with, you should only tackle one of the exercises and separate them off. For the difficult exercises, you could, for example, just concentrate on the heaviness of your left arm, then the right arm, then introduce the legs into the exercise. Once you feel, that you have mastered the exercise, you can increase the training phase by one aspect of the following exercises. Repeat the individual formula during the exercise 3 – 6 times in your head. In order to achieve quick results, you should do the exercise every day for at least five minutes, and if possible, several times a day.

Duration: 5 - 20 Minutes

Preparation:
Prepare a relaxed environment without distractions at a comfortable temperature.

You can do the exercises either sitting or lying down.

If your chair has arms, you can rest on them lightly. Your feet should be placed firmly on the ground. Your thighs and calves should be at a right angle to each other.

Execution:

The training begins with the first formula, the calmness formula. Close your eyes and say the following words to yourself: "I am completely calm." This formula is not really a part of the exercise, it is more like a preparation for the exercises, which are to follow.

You can decide for yourself, if you prefer to see the words written down or to listen to them in your head.

Now imagine a pendulum swinging backwards and forwards about a meter in front of you. In your mind, follow the movement of the pendulum. Concentrate on the swinging movement and notice how you are starting to relax.

Once the muscle relaxation exercise is in progress, the second formula, the heaviness exercise, can start:

1. Remember the basic formula and say to yourself "I am completely calm".

2. Now imagine, that your right arm is very heavy and concentrate on saying the formula to yourself about three times.

3. Repeat with your left arm.

4. Now imagine, that both arms are heavy and say the formula about three times to yourself.

5. Now, both legs are heavy. Concentrate your thoughts on the heaviness of your legs about three times.

6. Now direct your attention to the weight of all your limbs and concentrate on their heaviness about three times.

7. After the exercise, you should carry out the "cancel" sequence and count to yourself backwards from 6 to 1.

   - On the count of 6, you feel awake and well. All your senses are registering reality once more.

   - On the count of 5, your arms will become lighter.

   - On the count of 4, your heartbeat becomes calm.

   - On the count of 3, your breath becomes calm.

- On the count of 2, the temperature on your forehead feels normal.

- On the count of 1, take a deep breath and open your eyes.

It is important, during the exercises, to imagine, that your limbs are already heavy and not that they will become heavy, as this can cause a sense of expectation.

You can try one of the other exercises if you like. They are all executed in the same way as the heaviness exercise.

- Chapter 9 -

TIPS FOR RELATIVES

This book is not only meant to be read by people, who suffer from hypochondria. I would also like to add this chapter with tips, how you can support your afflicted relative. His social network is one of the most important supports for those, who are suffering from hypochondria. Without it, the self-help programme is only half as effective.

As a relative, you have already taken the first step. You have been collecting informative material, such as this book, so that you can understand the condition better. That is fundamental in understanding the difficulties affecting someone, who is close to you, or being able to put yourself in that person's position.

Firstly, I want to emphasise, that your relative, or close friend, is not an imaginary invalid. This person is sick. His sickness causes him as much anxiety as when he was suffering from a serious illness. To you, his anxiety and fears may seem excessive or irrational. However, in his eyes, this anxiety is real. This means, that he feels the physical symptoms in his body. He is not making up the symptoms in order to gain attention, he is really feeling them. This is why it is so difficult to get rid of the fear. It feels real.

- Do not encourage the sufferer by supporting his fears through explanations and you should avoid giving him tips, like suggesting he should go to the doctor. It is better to encourage him to find a therapist, more specifically to a cognitive behavioural therapist.

- Avoid asking him about his symptoms. This diverts his attention towards his body and his ailments. It is more useful to divert his attention towards other things.

- If your relative keeps asking whether you believe he is ill, remind him, that you believe his problem has more to do with his fears than a physical condition.

- Perhaps your relative has stopped taking part in the sporting activities, which he used to do, for fear of damaging his body, and perhaps he is staying at home more often. Encourage him to do some physical exercise. It is possible, that he could be more motivated, if you do something together with him. Perhaps you could go to the swimming pool together or go jogging? Sporting activity will help him to get the feeling back into his body and relieve his symptoms, which could possibly be the result of not having enough exercise.

- Be patient. It is not easy to find the right measure of attention and resistance to having conversations about sicknesses. Tread lightly and do not expect too much from him. Show him, that you are there and you are with him.

- It is possible, that he turns away from you, because he does not feel, that you are taking him seriously. Do not give up. Keep trying to find access to him and show him, that you want to help.

In the hypochondriacal phase, the sufferer's social interactions are often dysfunctional. They often feel as if they are not understood and they retreat into themselves. Remember, that this is part of the pathology and, when they are on the road to recovery, they will be grateful, I that you were there for them during the difficult times.

- Chapter 10 -

SUMMARY

We all have a little hypochondria within us. Who can say with honesty, that he or she has not read about some sickness and suddenly felt, that he or she has also had the same symptoms? Normally, this feeling goes away quickly. It is different with a hypochondriacal disorder. There is a fine line between normal fears and those fears, which can develop into hypochondria.

I became aware of how important it is to recognise this disorder as quickly as possible, in order to have the best chance of success with self-healing. The sooner you recognise the symptoms, the better. I am very grateful, that I have conquered it myself, without many therapy sessions, and I am able to say that, today I am healthy, without having had to stay in a special clinic.

The self-test helps me, even today, to check how I am doing. During the time, that I was filled with hypo-chondriacal thoughts, I was answering the questions with "yes" 7 times, which was a very strong indication of a disorder. I still find the self-test useful for checking on myself in an objective way. Of course, that always depends on answering the questions honestly.

These days, I understand much better what hypochondria is and have been able to develop my own strategy for recognising and overcoming this disorder. Today, I know, that I have a tendency to interpret physical symptoms wrongly in stress situations. My affirmations and relaxation techniques help me to prevent that from happening. These days I am able to understand well whether there is danger, or if I am getting worked up about nothing, or if it is a normal, brief health issue.

Progressive Muscle Relaxation and autogenic training are sometimes not recommended in text books, or only after consultation with a physician. This seems to be the case with serious disorders or delusional hypochondriacal disorders. Personally, I find Progressive Muscle Relaxation and autogenic training to be very good methods of relaxation. However, I only used it in the stabilisation phase and only after consultation with my doctor. If these techniques cause anxiety and agitation instead of promoting relaxation, you should probably try another form of exercise to relax.

Everyone learns differently. Perhaps you find it difficult to relax or impossible to concentrate on your technique. There is the possibility of guidance from an expert, or there are courses you can attend. There is also a lot of CDs or DVDs, which can guide you through the exercises by providing a voice, which tells you what to do in every step. This can help you at the beginning, particularly if you have not yet internalised the exercises.

You can also regain your body sensation and inner peace with the help of yoga and meditation. I have not gone into detail with these forms of relaxation because they are both such wide-ranging subjects, that they are too big to fit into this book. In addition, these techniques are better known than those, which I have explained here. Yoga and meditation can be practised either alone or in groups, with or without guidance from a specialist.

These relaxation techniques are well-known methods of relieving stress and anxiety. They are also used widely by healthy people, who have integrated them into their lives in order to escape from everyday stresses and regain a feeling of relaxation. In the meantime, there are many studies, which verify the effectiveness of Progressive Muscle Relaxation, autogenic training, yoga and meditation.

Perhaps you noticed in my personal story how important my mother was during this time and, of course, still is. Relatives are always important for support and this is why I recommend not only sufferers but also their relatives to read this book in order to develop an understanding of the issue and to provide a guide how to support your loved ones most effectively.

Self-treatment was the road to success for me. I am now free of fears and know the risks that relapses can trigger. I found a way to modify my behaviour and my way of thinking, using techniques, which are similar to those used in professional therapies. However, my personal experience does not mean, that my way is suitable for everyone. Depending on the severity of the condition or in cases with a traumatic background, it could be that self-help is not enough. If that is the situation, finding professional help is unavoidable.

Of course, I hope that this is not the case with you and that my book will help you to master your condition and help you understand how much you can benefit by the relaxation techniques.

I wish you much strength and success along the way so that you can regain the quality of your life, being able to tackle life full of vitality and serenity, and staying free of anxiety.

DID YOU ENJOY MY BOOK?

Now you have read my book, you know how to deal with hypochondria and what you need to know about this disorder. This is why I am asking you now for a small favour. Customer reviews are an important part of every product offered by Amazon. It is the first thing that customers look at and, more often than not, is the main reason whether or not they decide to buy the product. Considering the endless number of products available at Amazon, this factor is becoming increasingly important.

If you liked my book, I would be more than grateful if you could leave your review by Amazon. How do you do that? Just click on the "Write a customer review"-button (as shown below), which you find on the Amazon product page of my book or your orders site:

Review this product

Share your thoughts with other customers

Write a customer review

Please write a short note explaining what you liked most and what you found to be most important. It will not take longer than a few minutes, promise!

Be assured, I will read every review personally. It will help me a lot to improve my books and to tailor them to your wishes.

For this I say to you:

Thank you very much!

Yours
Lutz

BOOK RECOMMENDATIONS

The Power of Breathing Techniques

Breathing Exercises for more Fitness, Health and Relaxation

We can survive for weeks without food and days without water, but only a few minutes without air.

Would it not be justified to presume that the air, which is more important for human survival than food or water, should live up to basic standards? How much air do we need for ideal breathing? And how should we breathe?

The amount of air that you breathe has the potential to change everything you believe about your body, your health and your performance.

In this book, you will discover the fundamental relationship between Oxygen and your body.

Increasing your Oxygen supply is not only healthy, it enables an increase in the intensity of your training and also reduces breathlessness. In short, you will notice an improvement in your health and more relaxation in your everyday life.

Look forward to reading a lot of background information, experience reports, step-by-step instructions and secret tips which are tailor-made to your breathing technique and help you to become fitter, healthier and more relaxed.

This book is available on Amazon!

LUTZ SCHNEIDER

LITHIUM

—— AND ——

LITHIUM CARBONATE

A MEDICINAL PRODUCT FOR DEPRESSION, ALZHEIMER AND DEMENTIA, FOR IMPROVING WELL-BEING AND MANAGING STRESS

100% EXPERT KNOWLEDGE

EXPERTEN GRUPPE VERLAG

MADE IN GERMANY

Lithium and Lithium Carbonate

A medicinal product for Depression, Alzheimer and Dementia, for improving well-being and managing stress

Lithium is mostly known for its use in batteries. Most people do not realise that it is also a trace element in our bodies.

Would it not be wonderful if you could fight sicknesses, such as depression or Alzheimer, and improve your well-being, if you just had a little more Lithium in your body? What if you did not have to do anything more than take a little more Lithium?

Lithium is an important component for all of us in achieving a lasting, healthy way of life. Clinical studies and scientific articles are speaking a clear language. Despite that, Lithium is suffering a niche existence by a large majority of pharmaceutical scientists and is hardly known by the broad population.

Even so, the advantages of Lithium, which lie in psychological and mental health sector, are obvious and it is easy to obtain and use.

In this book, you will discover the advantages and effects of Lithium on your body and mind.

Read about fascinating background information, scientific findings, experience reports and secret tips which are tailor-made for your needs and which will help you to achieve a healthy, longer and more fulfilling life.

This book is available on Amazon!

SORBITOL INTOLERANCE

LIVING BETTER WITH SORBITOL INTOLERANCE – BACKGROUND, TUTORIALS, NUTRITIONAL ADJUSTMENT, RECIPES

100% EXPERT KNOWLEDGE

EXPERTEN GRUPPE VERLAG

MADE IN GERMANY

LUTZ SCHNEIDER

Sorbitol Intolerance

Living better with Sorbitol intolerance – background, tutorials, nutritional adjustment, recipes

Sorbitol intolerance is one of the least known food intolerances among many. And that, even though more and more people are suffering from it.

Wouldn't it be wonderful if you could at last find out if you suffer from Sorbitol intolerance? And how can you eat a diverse and delicious diet, despite your Sorbitol intolerance?

An increasing amount of industrially prepared food means that more and more people are taking doses of Sorbitol which they are not able to digest properly. This leads to a large number of lingering symptoms which are difficult to assign to any particular substance.

In this book you will find a simple guide on how to change your diet and a lot of important information about the subject of Sorbitol.

Read about fascinating background information, scientific findings, experience reports and secret tips which are tailor-made for you relating to your Sorbitol intolerance and which are designed to help you to achieve a healthy, longer and more fulfilling life.

This book is available on Amazon!

REFERENCES

Hypochondrie: Leibbezogenheit, Risikoverhalten,
Entwicklungsdynamik; mit 5 Tabellen
von Feldmann, Harald, 1972

Kognitive Verhaltenstherapie bei Hypochondrie und
Krankheitsangst
4. Aufl. 2019, von Bleichhardt, Gaby, 2019

Hypochondrie und Krankheitsangst
1. Aufl., von Bleichhardt, Gaby Martin, Alexandra,
2010

Die Welt der Hypochonder: über die älteste Krankheit
der Menschen
Ungekürzte Ausg., von Baur, Susan, 1994

Kognitive Verhaltenstherapie bei Hypochondrie und
Krankheitsangst: mit 12 Tab
3., vollst. überarb. und aktualisierte Aufl., von
Bleichhardt, Gaby Weck, Florian, 2015

Somatisierungsstörung und Hypochondrie
von Rief, Winfried Hiller, Wolfgang, 1998

Multiple somatoforme Symptome und Hypochondrie:
empirische Beiträge zur Diagnostik und Behandlung
1. Aufl., von Rief, Winfried, 1995

Hypochondrie
erschienen in PiD - Psychotherapie im Dialog,
01.12.2016

Welche Strategie hilft bei Hypochondrie?
von Witthöft, Michael, erschienen in InFo Neurologie
& Psychiatrie, 01.12.2017

Hypochondrie; Versuch einer konzeptionellen
Zusammenfassung
von Nissen, Bernd, erschienen in Forum der
Psychoanalyse, 01.03.2010

Hypochondrie – krankheitsangst
von Schmidt-Göhrich, Uta Katharina, 01.01.2016

http://www.psychosoziale-
gesundheit.net/psychiatrie/hypochondrie.html

https://www.netdoktor.de/krankheiten/hypochondri
e/

https://www.vigo.de/rubriken/krankheit-und-therapie/psyche-und-sucht/lesen/hypochondrie.html

https://de.wikipedia.org/wiki/Hypochondrie

https://www.meine-gesundheit.de/krankheit/krankheiten/hypochondrie

https://www.aerzteblatt.de/archiv/79602/Krankheits angst-Keine-Bagatelle

https://www.123test.com/de/Neurotizismus-Emotionale-Stabilit%C3%A4t/

https://www.lernen.net/artikel/gefuehlskaelte-alexithymie-3642/

https://www.beobachter.ch/gesundheit/krankheit/hy pochondrie

https://www.zeit.de/zeit-wissen/2011/04/Hypochondrie

https://d-nb.info/1114067601/34

https://clearsound.de/hypochonder-eingebildete-kranke/

http://www.hypochonder24.de/hypochondrie-besiegen/index.html

https://www.medizin-im-text.de/blog/2017/5936/tipps-gegen-hypochondrie/

https://minddrops.de/infos/progressive-muskelentspannung/

https://wiki.yoga-vidya.de/Progressive_Muskelentspannung

https://www.refinery29.com/de-de/autogenes-training-formeln-uebungen

http://www.gesundheits-lexikon.com/Therapie/Autogenes-Training/

https://www.angst-panik-hilfe.de/angst-krankheiten-angehoerige.html

DISCLAIMER